How Animals Brought Fire to People

by Maryann Dobeck

illustrated by Mark Schroder

Table of Contents

Chapter 1

The Old Man and Woman

One cold night the storyteller sat by the fire. Sitting with him were the native Indians of northern California. They liked the storyteller very much. And they liked his technique of storytelling. He told them wonderful tales. His stories seemed to hum with excitement.

"Please tell us a story," the native people pleaded.

The storyteller smiled. He said, "Look at this roaring fire we have. I'll tell you the story of how fire was given to all people."

In the beginning, only an old
man and woman had Fire. They were
supposed to share Fire with the native
Indians. But the old ones were greedy.
They kept Fire all to themselves. Try as
they might, no one could get Fire away
from them.

The old man and woman were mean
and frightful. Each time the native people
approached their hut to ask them for
Fire, the old ones drove them away.

The old man and woman would make fearsome faces. They would open their eyes wide and stare at anyone who came near them. Then the old ones would growl or hiss. They exposed their teeth so that they looked like wild dogs about to attack. Just the sight of them was enough to scare everyone away.

The two old people looked almost as frightening when they weren't trying to scare anyone. They both had long, stringy hair tied up in a knot. Their faces were long and lean, deeply wrinkled with age. They were missing the majority of their teeth. The old woman had only four crooked teeth in the front of her down-turned mouth. The old man had five pointed teeth, with one broken off at the tip.

The old ones were tall and thin. In fact, they were so thin that when they walked, they rattled like bags of bones. Their yellowish skin hung down as though it were coming unglued. The old man and woman were truly a frightening sight.

Chapter 2
Coyote Helps the Indians

On the coldest night of the winter, the Indians went to see Coyote. They knew Coyote was very clever. They begged him to steal Fire from the old ones. Coyote hatched a plan.

Coyote marked a trail from the land of the native people to the old people's hut. He placed animals along the way. He put the strongest animal near the hut. He put the weakest one the farthest away. He hid an Indian near the hut.

Coyote had told everyone exactly what they had to do and when they had to do it. Then he went to the hut to see the old man and woman.

When Coyote arrived, he made sure the Indian was hidden nearby. Then Coyote knocked softly on the door. No one answered. So Coyote knocked again and again. Each time he knocked harder and harder.

Finally, the old woman unlatched the door, holding a club in her hand. "Get out of here!" she cried.

"It's so cold that I'm freezing to death," said Coyote. "Please, please let me sit by your fire and warm up for a while." Coyote was a cunning animal. He began to shake his body as if shivering from the cold.

The old woman thought about it for a moment, then let Coyote in. "You can sit by the fire for now," she sneered. "But you can't stay long."

Coyote sat by the fire with the old ones. Then he waited for the Indian and all the animals to do their part.

As planned, the Indian hiding near the hut began his attack. He pounded and pounded on the door with his heavy club. "Come out here, old man and woman!" he yelled.

The old people rushed out to investigate what was happening. With the Indian distracting them at the door, Coyote was quickly able to grab a long flaming stick from the fire. Then he raced out of the hut and down the trail.

The angry old man and woman chased Coyote. As they caught up to him, Coyote looked around for his helpers.

Chapter 3
Bringing Fire to Everyone

Suddenly, Mountain Lion leaped from where he was hiding in the bushes. He grabbed the flaming stick from Coyote and raced as fast as he could. But he was no match for the thin, bony old man and woman. They were so lightweight that they could run much faster than he could.

Soon the old ones were right behind Mountain Lion. He could feel their hot breath and hear their loud cries of "Stop, thief! Stop!" Mountain Lion knew he would be caught. It was an awful feeling.

Bear was hidden in a cave, waiting for Mountain Lion to run by. Then it was Bear's turn to spring into action. Just as the old ones were about to catch Mountain Lion, Bear jumped out of the cave. He grabbed the flaming stick from Mountain Lion and ran on.

Bear was a fast runner. He knew how important it was to keep the flaming stick safe. He did not want to get caught. Bear ran quickly from the old ones, but he wasn't as fast as Mountain Lion. Soon the old ones were catching up to Bear.

The old man and woman almost caught Bear. Just as they reached out for him, he saw Rabbit up ahead. Rabbit was the next animal on the trail. She was waiting for Bear to run by.

"Catch!" yelled Bear, throwing the flaming stick to Rabbit. His aim was perfect. Rabbit jumped up, caught the stick, and ran off with it along the trail.

The flame burned the whiskers on poor Rabbit's face, but she ran on and on. The old ones ran on faster than ever. They were faster than Rabbit.

The flaming stick continued from one animal to another along the trail. Coyote's plan was insightful. He had picked the fastest animals he could find to move the flaming stick along the trail. But the old man and woman were faster than all of them. One by one, they caught up to Coyote, Mountain Lion, Bear, and all the others.

Squirrel was the next to the last animal on the trail leading to the village. By the time he got the flaming stick, it had burned far down. Squirrel ran with the stick, being careful not to burn his paws.

Squirrel handed the flaming stick off to Frog, the last animal. Frog hopped along as fast as he could. But he wasn't fast enough to outrun the old ones.

As the old man and woman came nearer, Frog was afraid they would catch him. Suddenly, the old woman reached out and grabbed him in her bony old hand.

Frog knew how hard everyone had worked, and he didn't want to let them down. He had to do something. So with one big gulp he swallowed the small stick of Fire.

Frog let out a big CROAK. It was the first one he ever made. The sound startled the old woman so much that she loosened her grip.

Frog broke loose and jumped into the river. He swam across until he reached the other side. The old ones could not reach him there.

Once on land, Frog spit out the Fire. It landed on some dry sticks. From that day on, because of Coyote's clever plan, the native people could make a fire by rubbing two sticks together.

Comprehension Check

Summarize

Use a Compare and Contrast chart to find details in the story that are the same and different. Then use the chart to summarize the story.

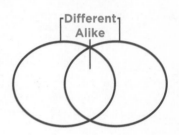

Think and Compare

1. Reread page 5. How were the old man and woman alike in appearance? How were they different? *(Compare and Contrast)*

2. Have you ever worked with a group to accomplish a goal? Tell about it. *(Apply)*

3. Why is it important for people to share with others? *(Evaluate)*